The
Nuffs, Not So Sure,
and the
Wanna Be's

The
Nuffs, Not So Sure,
and the
Wanna Be's

A Fairy Tale for Adult Children

by
Elaine M. Bready

Creative Resources

Art Illustrations by Alyce J. Blue

Volume 1 of the "Nuff Stories" Series

We gratefully acknowledge permission to print the poem, "Five," Copyright © 1991 by Adrienne R. Mervin

Creative Resources
Mona L. Jeter, Publisher
P.O. Box 2318, North Highlands, California 95660
Requests for orders should be addressed to Post Office Box 2318, North Highlands, California 95660. (916) 344-7546.

Printed in the United States of America
First Edition

ISBN: 1-880388-51-0

Dedication

To
the wonder
of all
of
our
children;
that we may
learn from
them
the miracle of
life and
the joy of
living.

Five

somewhere, in another place and time,
you and i met ...
was it on the kindergarten playground?
each of us sat silently alone,
fervently building our sand fortresses,
to keep the loneliness away

beneath your stoic exterior
lies such depth,
such power,
so many feelings -
it is all so familiar ...

has the time come
for us to stop naming our "lost-ness"
and start allowing ourselves to
be found?

we shall meet again,
all grown-up
knowing
where we have been hiding
and why

come out into the sunshine with me,
my friend ...
it's only fear
that has kept us alone.

- Adrienne R. Mervin

Acknowledgments

Many wonderful people have worked hard to make this book possible. My heartfelt gratitude to each of you. My special thank you to Lois, Mona, Sharon, Alyce, and Adrienne for their courage, strength, and willingness to walk the path of rediscovering and reclaiming our wounded inner children together. It hasn't been nearly as scary for me with you by my side. Thank you to Dixie and Nancy at Griffin Printing for your continued support, guidance, and professionalism. Your smiles, warmth, and humor was comforting to my insecure inner child. My deepest appreciation to the men and women who took the risk to introduce me to their own wounded children and allowed me to share my gifts to assist their own healing journey.

And above all, my eternal gratitude to my own guardian angels and Higher Power who allowed me to be the messenger of this wonderful, miraculous message.

Foreword

Fairy tales assist children with learning valuable lessons, while stimulating the creative side of young intellect. To grasp the meaning of any story requires only imagination, some quiet time, and a willingness to explore the sometimes permeable boundaries of reality.

For whatever reasons, many of us knew childhoods marked with such a deep sense of rigidity and responsibility that left no room for frivolous fairy tales. Now, as adult children, we have difficulty believing in intangible things, do not know how to simply stand still, and are waiting for permission to entertain the magical possibility of change.

The Nuffs, Not So Sure, and the Wanna Be's are such adult children; their journey to change a wounding reality may also be yours. I chose to return to the City of Free To Be through self-inspection, re-defining some truths with the wonder and honesty of a child. The quest is not without obstacles, but is unlike any other path to personal freedom.

Thank you Elaine, my sister and friend, for putting into words the journey of so many. Like Feeler, I have always known there was a better way - I needed only to trust my heart.

Adrienne R. Mervin

Dear Reader,

All of my life I have experienced a sense of loss, of not belonging, of being alone. This feeling was experienced at the deepest level of my being. It was experienced at a level beyond my multi-cultural identity, beyond my sexual identity, beyond any perceived childhood trauma. Yet, outwardly, it did not appear to others that I carried this sense of loss. I have been relatively successful in my chosen work, relatively happy with myself, and relatively content with my place in this great world. Most of the time, my relative comfort would disguise and deny that deep sense of emptiness. There were times, quiet alone times, when I wondered why I was so afraid of making a mistake or of failing. I wondered why I felt the tremendous need to be in control. It was difficult for me to cry openly; to be angry without being enraged or feeling such guilt. I wondered why my joy was so short-lived. I worried about there not being enough - enough love, support, food, money, success, etc. Through a series of personal and professional crises, I came to realize that what I was really saying was that I was not enough for me.

It is both a startling revelation and a painful contradiction to my whole way of living. Part of me understood and lived life as though I was more than enough. Part of me desperately needed more. This contradiction and conflict was present in my professional, my interpersonal, and personal relationships. There came a growing sense that everything needed to change, yet nothing needed to change.

Through a series of educational seminars, counseling, and exercises, I discovered a deep disconnection between myself and the little girl I once was. I came to understand how I had abandoned her in my attempt to prevent further pain. I came to understand my sense of loss. I was able to acknowledge and accept all the ways I tried to compensate for that loss, only to create a deeper hole in my heart.

I have since reclaimed my abandoned inner child. Our bond is a healing one. I no longer search outside myself for solutions to an emptiness. I no longer feel empty. I no longer live life with scarcity. Instead, I feel fulfilled and whole - emotionally, physically, and most importantly spiritually. Life is a joyous, wonderful journey. Each day is a miracle for me and my inner child. Together we make a difference for ourselves. Together, I know we can make a difference for others.

The Nuffs, Not So Sure, and the Wanna Be's represent each of us as we journey to wholeness. Our paths may be filled with many obstacles as a result of the dysfunctional way we learned to live life. But deep within us all is a common yearning to return to a time where we were free to be.

It is my hope that through the Nuff Stories Series that you and your inner child can experience the wonder of you. I know that your whole way of living can be enhanced. Together, you two can make a difference.

Love and Peace,

Elaine M. Bready

The
Nuffs, Not So Sure,
and the
Wanna Be's

Once upon a time in a faraway land, there was a beautiful city where only children lived and played. The sky above was filled with a hundred rainbows. The sun's rays bounced brightly from these rainbows onto the city below casting beautiful colors of violet, blue, green, orange, red, and yellow. The city was filled with many magnificent parks and playgrounds. Clowns, puppeteers, mimes, and magicians could be found on every street corner. The air was filled with the scents of flowers and fruit trees. Butterflies and birds glided freely on the currents of gentle breezes. Flutes and harps sang their joyful tunes throughout the land.

The laughter and squeals of joyful children could be heard for quite a distance. Many, many people came from miles away to watch the children from the gates of the city. These big people were never permitted to stay long or to join in the fun because the city had been created for children under five years old. It was a magical, mystical city created by the wise old men and women who were the children's guardian angels. The angels named the city "Free To Be."

These angels lovingly guarded the magnificent gates of Free To Be City while enjoying the love and laughter of the city's inhabitants. Love, peace, and harmony were in and around everyone. Long ago, they had decided to create a special place where children could live and grow free from the "Should's," "Have-To's," and the "Ought-To-Be's."

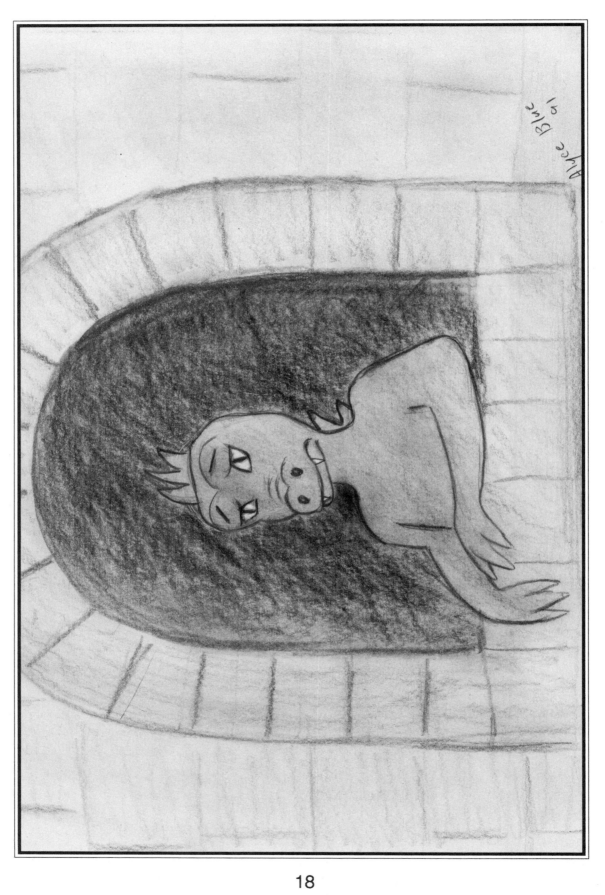

18

Now the Should's, Have-To's, and Ought-To-Be's were dragons that lived outside the city in the bare deserts surrounding Free To Be. The big people who crowded the gates watching the children lived in the land ruled by these dragons. The dragons were not really mean, but they insisted on having many rules.

"Rules are necessary to bring order and equality," they remarked.

"People are much happier when they know what should happen, what they have to do, and how they ought to be," said one leader named *Know What's Best.*

"I agree," said another called *Do What's Right.* **"No one will ever doubt how things should be with these clear messages. No one will be different, better, or worse. No one will be special."**

Do What I Say, another leader, rose up on his giant legs and stretched. **"Yes, I agree. Everyone needs our rules. In the long run, people will be much happier."**

These dragon leaders gathered every morning to proclaim these same thoughts. Feeling quite justified, they would then set off on their way checking on the big people living in Realworld City.

On this particular day, a fourth leader called *Not So Sure* sat by the window of the meeting room thoughtfully gazing at the big people below.

"I wonder," she thought aloud, **"if all those chains and collars the big people are wearing really make them feel secure? Is it possible that the sacks of Should's, Have-To's, and Ought-To-Be's rocks get so heavy that these big people become tired and unhappy? Why don't we see smiles? Why don't we hear laughter? Can they really be happy?"**

All of the other leaders turned suddenly at the door and glared

at *Not So Sure.*

"**What a stupid thing to ask!**" they bellowed.

"**This is the way it's always been!**" exclaimed *Do What I Say.* **We were all taught this way and look how good we turned out!**" yelled *Know What's Best.*

Softly, *Do What's Right* said, "**I know that they may not be smiling and jumping for joy, but,**" she continued, "**you really have to have faith in them. They know that this is Realworld City and life should be hard. After all, life ought to build strong characters. Now enough of this kind of talk - we really have to check on the big people.**"

Do What I Say agreed. "**Yes, *Not So Sure,* surely you would not want them to fail - would you? It really is for their own good, you know. Come now, let's do what we have to, what we should do, and what we ought to do. We do have a big responsibility.**"

"**There really isn't a choice. If we change the rules now, what will they think of us?**" asked *Know What's Best.* With that, he gently nudged *Not So Sure* out of the room.

Together, they went about their business of making sure all the big people in Realworld City followed all of the rules that would make them happy, secure, and successful. Still, *Not So Sure* was not completely convinced. However, she reluctantly accompanied her colleagues as they met with the city's army leaders.

Realworld City needed a large army to control these big people because there were always some people who wanted to disobey and break the rules. So the army used the talents of teachers like Anger, Fear, Guilt, Shame, Blame, and Wrongness to help them control the people better. These teachers were very successful and so the dragon leaders encouraged the methods used by the army and its teachers.

§ § §

This is the way the big people lived for many hundreds of years. For many, the longer they lived this way, the more comfortable they became. Of course, they hadn't always lived this way ... for all the big people once lived in Free To Be City until the age of five.

At five, children passed through the gates into Realworld City so that they could become productive members of the whole society. The children were not afraid of this because it was just the way things were. It was all part of growing up. They all longed to grow up so that they could be the best that they could be - just like the big people. Still, there was some sadness at having to leave a place of such freedom and joy. For many children, the memories of Free To Be were tucked away safely in their hearts and souls. So as they exited the gates of their city into Realworld City, many changes began to happen.

Something very mysterious happened to the children as they entered the gates of their new home. The gates of Realworld City were always covered in a dense, gray fog. As they walked through the fog, they began to forget their experiences in Free To Be City. As each memory faded, a new thought took its place. These new thoughts were about doing what's right, following the advice of the leaders, and practicing the ways of the older ones.

One of the first lessons of their schooling was that feelings should not be expressed. This was sometimes a painful lesson to learn because Anger, Fear, Guilt, Shame, Blame, and Wrongness taught the lessons in a way that the children could not forget. Anger and Fear worked together to show the children that if you let your feelings out, others would be so angry that something terrible would happen. Of course, the children had to try it to find out. Because they had been living in Free To Be, they had not learned to control certain feelings. When Anger and Fear showed them what happened when they expressed their feelings, the pain was so deep that the children learned to keep their feelings inside.

The children learned from Shame and Blame that they were just like everyone else. They were not special and if they acted different or special, well, they would be humiliated and accused of terrible things. Once again, the pain struck deep inside, but because Anger and Fear were standing nearby, they kept quiet about their feelings.

Guilt and Wrongness helped the children to see all the things that they <u>should</u> do, that they <u>have</u> to do, and <u>ought</u> to do. The children learned these things by trying to do and be different things. For example, they might try to clean their rooms. After cleaning the rooms, Guilt and Wrongness would criticize, saying things like, **"You don't care about all of the nice things in your room. Look at how you take care of your things. You can't do anything right, can you?"**

Well, after several times, the children got the idea that whatever they did, they <u>should</u> do it better. Sometimes, the older ones would not hug them or comfort them because they really had been so wrong or so stupid. Sometimes they ended up feeling like nothing they did was ever right. They knew then that feelings didn't matter. What mattered was doing the <u>right</u> thing, the <u>right</u> way. Of course, no one ever showed them the right way. They were only criticized for the way they did things.

It wasn't that the older ones didn't love them or didn't want to comfort them. The older ones were afraid of being loving or comforting because they knew it was against the rules of Realworld City. They also remembered the pain in their hearts and did not want to feel it again. So, oftentimes they said and did exactly what they were taught by these powerful teachers. Yet, deep inside, just like the younger ones, they secretly knew that this was not a happy place. They didn't know what could be done, just that this was the ways things were, and that things would all work out for the best. They believed the message of the dragon leaders because the dragon leaders always knew what was best. They also believed that one day, if they followed all of the rules, that they would be happy once again. They believed this because it was the promise given them by the dragon leaders.

Almost everyone in Realworld City secretly felt deep inside that something was missing; but they never talked about it because Fear, Shame, and Guilt were always close by. So, no one really knew that so many people shared the same feelings.

§ § §

Now, in every city, there are always a few that just can't seem to follow the rules. There are those who won't believe everything that is said. In Realworld City, these people were called the *Nuffs*. The dragon leaders were always concerned about the *Nuffs* and did everything they could to control them. It seemed though, that no matter what the *Nuffs* experienced, they kept getting up, time and time again, to fight for what they believed.

The *Nuffs* were the only ones who remembered Free To Be City. Somehow, the fog at the gates was not able to completely erase their memories. The *Nuffs* longed to return to Free To Be and felt that everyone had a right to be free. They tried to seek out others who might feel the way that they did, but it was not an easy thing to do.

Many *Nuffs* had to endure abuse, neglect, abandonment, rejection, shame, blame, guilt, wrongness, and fear. They tried many things to overcome these experiences. They tried to be invisible. They tried to please everyone. They tried to be over-achievers. They even tried to be rebellious. No matter what they tried, they were always punished. Instead of giving in, they became stronger inside, and the desire to be free grew more intense.

Because feelings can't be locked up forever, several *Nuffs* secretly got together one day and began to share what they were feeling and thinking. It was so exciting to discover that there were others who had the same thoughts and feelings. Through their

meetings, they began to realize that there really was a possibility of returning to Free To Be and they began to explore ways that might help them return to the place where they began many years ago.

As excited as they were, they were also afraid. There were many, many obstacles to face. Even though they believed that they could do it, no one was sure exactly how to go about getting there.

§ § §

Now the wise old men and women who guarded the gates of Free To Be City spoke with other angels who wanted to help the *Nuffs*. They had watched the things that had happened to them, and felt all of the pain that the *Nuffs* had endured. One day, the guardian angels called a meeting of all concerned angels. During this meeting, it was decided that many of these guardian angels would begin to offer guidance and support to the *Nuffs*.

"Everyone should be entitled to live life as they choose!" they exclaimed. **"There is plenty of love, joy, and peace for all,"** they remarked. **"Actually, if everyone knew the special wonder and purpose of his or her existence, the world could at least be the way the Creator had designed it."**

So it was decided that every *Nuff* would be assigned a guardian angel. The *Nuffs* would begin to experience dreams, thoughts, and feelings that would open the windows of remembrance. The windows of remembrance would provide the *Nuffs* with the tools and skills that would help them to return to Free To Be City. As the *Nuffs* began to remember more and more, each guardian angel could give more and more help to the *Nuffs*. The guardian angels knew that this was a good and safe way to help the *Nuffs*. They knew that if they came into the *Nuffs'* lives and brought them to the city themselves, it would be too much of a shock. The angels also knew that if they did all the work, the *Nuffs* would never know how strong, how good or how wise they really were. The angels also knew, that knowing deep inside, your own strengths, goodness, and wisdom is the key to returning to Free To Be.

Other angels chose to remain in Free To Be to help the city's children prepare for the return of the big people. The children worked together with the angels polishing and cleaning and making other preparations for the big people. Just as the meeting was ending, one angel thought aloud: **"This will be very difficult for the *Nuffs*. I think we should find an ally for them from among Realworld's leaders. What do you think?"**

"What a splendid idea!" said another angel. **"Suppose we ask *Not So Sure* to help us help them? Surely she is beginning to doubt the methods of the old way of doing things. Why, just think of her compassion as she spoke of the big people the other day. I believe she is the one."**

"Very good. Let us then begin to send love and joy to her heart and she will do the rest," said one angel joyfully.

Another angel gazed thoughtfully at the other angels and said, **"Still, there must be a way for her to reach the *Nuffs* - a way that the *Nuffs* can recognize her as an ally. Any suggestions?"**

After some discussion, a novice angel blurted out, **"Perhaps, we can send the same love and light to the *Nuffs* and among them will emerge several leaders, teachers, and healers that can see beyond the anger, fear, guilt, and blame to the compassion that lives within *Not So Sure's* heart."**

"Wonderful, wonderful," they all remarked.

"Let us go then in peace and love and begin our work," said the eldest angel.

The angels left the meeting with soul-felt love, compassion, and harmony to begin the task of opening the windows of remembrance for the *Nuffs.*

§ § §

That night, laying quietly in his bed, a *Nuff* called *Dreamer* gazed at the full moon outside his window. *Dreamer* spent many nights gazing at the sparkling stars wondering what it might be like to soar among them. As he drifted off to sleep, he began to experience a thought that this was indeed possible. He dreamed that night of being able to teach others how to fly.

Not far away, his sister *Feeler* lay wondering how wonderful it must feel to be free. She began to dream of a strange land where she found herself picking flowers, leaves, and rocks and giving them to others. When she did this, people began to smile and to feel happiness.

The next morning, the *Nuffs* whispered among themselves and spoke of the curious dreams, thoughts, and feelings each had experienced. These events continued to happen every night; and every morning the *Nuffs* shared their experiences. Growing within them was an excitement and wonder. They began to look forward to their dreams. Some even took time during the day to think and feel all of the thoughts and feelings that would come.

At about the same time, *Not So Sure* also began to have dreams. These dreams spoke of the pain and sorrow in the hearts of the big people. She felt these things so deeply that she began to think of ways to ease the pain for them. She awoke each morning dreading the daily meetings of the dragon leaders. She grew more and more restless listening to the justifications of the old way. **"Surely, there must be another way to live,"** she thought. **"But, what other way?"**

The other leaders began to grow very uncomfortable with *Not So Sure.* They brought in Anger, Fear, Guilt, Shame, and many of the teachers of the old way to help them control *Not So Sure.* They spoke of the Should's, Have-To's, and Ought-To-Be's. They reminded her of her responsibility and duty to the old ways and the tradition of their ancestors. Still, *Not So Sure* could not shake the feelings in her heart. So, in disgust and frustration, they threw up their hands and left. They wanted to replace her with someone else. But they knew that if they did that, the big people in the city would think that something was really wrong. They were absolutely sure that they were not wrong nor were the old ways. So they decided to just ignore *Not So Sure.* They believed that since she was only one dragon, she could do no harm. After all, one dragon could never make a difference.

At first, *Not So Sure* felt hurt and rejected. Later, she realized that this was exactly the way they wanted her to feel so that she would return to the old way of thinking. Instead, she went off by herself and spent many lonely hours by Tree that grew alone in the desert. She began to see herself much like her new friend, Tree. Both of them were determined to grow in spite of the loneliness and the dreariness of their surroundings.

§ § §

One late afternoon, just as the sun was setting on the horizon of the desert, *Not So Sure* walked slowly toward her friend Tree. As she approached, she saw two *Nuffs* laying quietly under Tree's branches. They seemed to be daydreaming - lost in the clouds that drifted by. Not wanting to frighten the *Nuffs*, she cleared her throat as she came upon them.

"Ahem..."

Startled out of their daydreams, *Dreamer* and *Feeler* sat up and stared at the dragon approaching them.

Suddenly many thoughts raced through their minds of what they should be doing, had to be doing, and ought to be doing. They quickly got up to leave when they heard *Not So Sure* speak.

"Don't be afraid. I have come to sit by my friend Tree to enjoy the shade and solitude. It is here that I feel peaceful and dream wonderful dreams of a life without Should's, Have-To's and Ought-To-Be's. Please do not go - join me. We can share Tree together."

Well, the two *Nuffs* could barely believe their ears. Here was a dragon leader speaking the words of their hearts.

"I am *Dreamer* and this is my sister *Feeler*," the older *Nuff* said confidently to *Not So Sure*.

"How is it that you know me?" asked *Not So Sure.*

"Uh, I'm not sure, but I heard your words in a dream and I knew they came from your heart. I heard the questions in your mind and knew that you weren't so sure about the way things are here in Realworld City," *Dreamer* explained.

"How is it that you are unafraid?" the doubtful dragon asked turning to *Feeler.*

"Well, I don't fear what you say because, I can feel what is in your heart. Your feelings are just like mine. I feel as though we have much in common," *Feeler* said timidly.

Having exchanged these thoughts, the three of them watched the sun disappear; and one by one, they drifted into a deep sleep.

Now the guardian angels were joyous at the sight of these three beings together. As they slept, the angels sent through dreams, special gifts of courage, love, compassion, perseverance

and remembrance. Among these gifts were the gifts of teaching, healing and leading. Each of them awakened from their dream refreshed and re-energized in a way that they had not experienced before.

Vowing to meet each other every day, they parted ways without speaking of the experiences each had dreamed of that day.

§ § §

Day after day, week after week, and month after month went by. The three companions spent hours speaking of the possibilities of returning to Free To Be City. They practiced the skills and exercises that each received through their dreams in their quiet moments spent alone. Secretly they began to share their thoughts, feelings, and skills with the other *Nuffs*. Even *Not So Sure* found other dragons that shared her inner feelings and desires. These dragons called themselves *Wanna Be's*.

Together, the *Nuffs, Not So Sure,* and the *Wanna Be's* had begun the journey that would return them to Free To Be City in the land of abundance. The guardian angels continued to send messages of love and peace. They celebrated each new awareness and offered hope to *Not So Sure*, the *Nuffs*, and the *Wanna Be's*. They were indeed joyous as they sensed the opening of the windows of remembrance. The children of Free To Be shouted words of encouragement to the *Nuffs* and the *Wanna Be's*.

One day, the guardian angels gathered together once again around the rainbow table.

"**You know**," remarked one wise old angel. "**If these messages can help the *Nuffs* and the *Wanna Be's,* then they could help many other beings. Perhaps, there are many who have not yet shared the thoughts of *Dreamer* or expressed their feelings like *Feeler* or spoken aloud the doubts of *Not So Sure* and the *Wanna Be's*. Perhaps we can provide these experiences, tools, and exercises for all beings to use as they are ready. Let us offer these things to all beings.**"

"**Splendid!**"

"**Marvelous!**"

"**Wonderful!**" the angels exclaimed. "**Let us make it so!**"

So the day came when the angels sent to all the inhabitants of Realworld City many ways of experiencing love, compassion, and hope. The wise old angels knew that there were many beings who carried painful holes in their hearts. They deeply wanted to help all beings to heal the holes in their hearts and to once again know that the gates are always open to those who want to be free.

The Beginning!

Big Elaine
and
Little Elaine

About the Author

I was born of Japanese, African-American, Native-American, and Caucasian-American descent. Being a female or multi-cultural is not significant in and of itself. Being born in the middle of a color and cultural continuum in our society was difficult and wounding to my sense of cultural identity. Being born female in our society was wounding to my sexual identity. Being born to two loving people who brought with them all of their own wounds and unhealed scars of this dysfunctional society was wounding to my inner spiritual identity. Alcoholism, abuse, and racism touched me in ways that left me searching all my life for the one person, the one accomplishment, the one solution that would fill the hole in my heart. I grew up in a rigid military family system within a rigid military environment. I married into that same dysfunctional system - not because I loved it, but because it was familiar. I was comfortable with being uncomfortable. My work with substance abuse, family violence, and cultural issues was a way to fix what was broken in our society. But it was more than that. It was my subconscious way of fixing the wounds in my soul. Throughout my marriage, my parenting, and my professional life, I have been giving to get. The ability to relate to the military, to alcoholics and drug addicts, to battered women and children, to the racially oppressed were gifts of my wounds. Still, no matter what I had accomplished, I was left with a deep sense of inadequacy. The day I became painfully aware that I was passing my wounds to my daughter - marked the beginning of my own discovery and recovery.

Rediscovering and reclaiming my own wounded inner child has given me a tremendous sense of wholeness, of completeness. My whole life has changed. I am fulfilled in all of my relationships because I have rediscovered the joy of living, the wonder of my existence, and the miracle of being free.

From the instant of my birth, my journey has been filled with lessons learned from everyone whose path I've crossed. It has been learning these lessons that broadens my journey. If you would like to share your thoughts, feelings or experiences with me, you may reach me by writing to this address:

Elaine M. Whitefeather
P.O. Box 292
Fair Oaks, CA 95628

For additional copies of <u>The Nuffs, Not So Sure, and the Wanna Be's</u> or <u>Healing the Holes in My Heart</u>, please write to:

Elaine M. Whitefeather
P.O. Box 292
N   Fair Oaks, CA 95628   50

Elaine Bready is also available for lectures, workshops, and to appear as a guest speaker in your area. Please contact us at the above address for further information.